Sisters

Sisters

Raina Telgemeier

with color by Braden Lamb

graphix

An Imprint of

SCHOLASTIC

For Amara, obviously

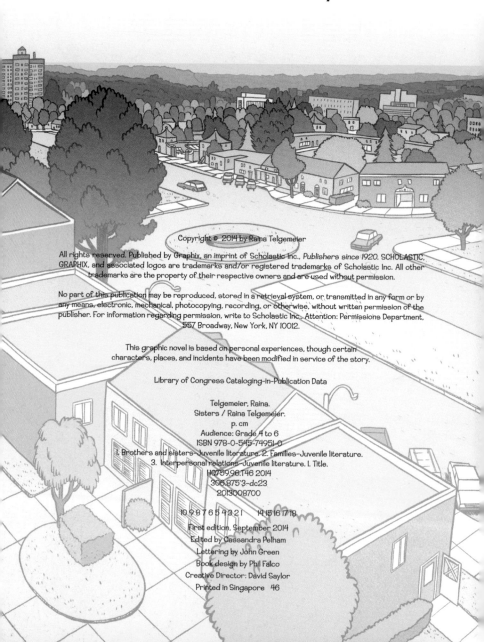

Copyright © 2014 by Raina Telgemeier

All rights reserved. Published by Graphix, an imprint of Scholastic Inc., Publishers since 1920. SCHOLASTIC, GRAPHIX, and associated logos are trademarks and/or registered trademarks of Scholastic Inc. All other trademarks are the property of their respective owners and are used without permission.

This graphic novel is based on personal experiences, though certain characters, places, and incidents have been modified in service of the story.

Library of Congress Cataloging-in-Publication Data

Telgemeier, Raina.
Sisters / Raina Telgemeier.
p. cm
Audience: Grade 4 to 6
ISBN 978-0-545-74951-0
1. Brothers and sisters–Juvenile literature. 2. Families–Juvenile literature. 3. Interpersonal relations–Juvenile literature. I. Title.
HQ759.96.T46 2014
306.875'3–dc23
2013008700

10 9 8 7 6 5 4 3 2 1   14 15 16 17 18

First edition, September 2014
Edited by Cassandra Pelham
Lettering by John Green
Book design by Phil Falco
Creative Director: David Saylor
Printed in Singapore 46

ARE YOU SURE YOU'RE ALL PACKED? YOU'RE NOT FORGETTING ANYTHING?

WHAT ABOUT THE TENT?

YES, I PACKED THE TENT.

WHAT ABOUT FLARES? BATTERIES? EXTRA WATER?

DENIS, WE'RE ONLY DRIVING FROM CALIFORNIA TO COLORADO!

YEAH, WHY ARE **YOU** SO STRESSED?

YOU'RE NOT EVEN COMING!

MAPS! DO YOU HAVE THE MAPS?

DADDY, WHY AREN'T YOU DRIVING TO AUNT MARY'S WITH US?

I'VE TOLD YOU, WILL . . .

I HAVE WORK THIS WEEK. MAKES MORE SENSE FOR ME TO TAKE A PLANE AND MEET YOU GUYS THERE.

OH.

ARE YOU EXCITED ABOUT SEEING YOUR COUSINS, RAINA?

I DUNNO.

WE HAVEN'T HAD A FAMILY REUNION IN ALMOST TEN YEARS!

I THOUGHT THAT WAS 'CAUSE YOU DIDN'T GET ALONG WITH YOUR SIBLINGS.

SPEAKING OF WHICH . . .

AMARA! RAINA!

HOW DO YOU EXPECT TO SURVIVE A WEEK IN THE CAR TOGETHER IF YOU CAN'T EVEN GET THROUGH **DINNER?**

I REALLY WISH YOU'D TAKE MY CAR INSTEAD. IT'S NEWER.

YOUR CAR IS TOO SMALL. MINE IS FINE.

I BET **YOU** WISH WE WERE TAKING DAD'S CAR, TOO...

ESPECIALLY CONSIDERING... "THE INCIDENT."

HAAA-HAAAH.

WHY DID I EVER ASK FOR A SISTER?!

SPLASH

MOM! DAD!

WHAT IS IT, HONEY?

Gasp
pant

I WANT A SISTER!!

6

RAINA . . . I'M GOING TO BE HAVING A BABY.

A GIRL?!

WELL . . . WE WON'T KNOW UNTIL IT GETS HERE.

IT BETTER BE A GIRL.

EITHER WAY, YOU'RE GOING TO BE A GOOD BIG SISTER!

YOU CAN HELP FEED THE BABY AND HOLD IT AND CARE FOR IT . . .

BUT SOON

HEY, MOM?

WHAT'S ALL THIS STUFF DOING IN MY ROOM?

7

A FEW MONTHS LATER

IT'S A CARD FOR WHEN MOM BRINGS THE BABY HOME FROM THE HOSPITAL, GRANDMA!

VERY NICE!

RING!

SHE DID? IT IS? I'LL PUT RAINA ON!

RAINA? IT'S DADDY! YOU HAVE A NEW BABY SISTER!

EEEEEEEEEEEEEEE!!!!!

WE'RE HEEERE!

RAINA, MEET YOUR **SISTER!**

YOU'RE SURE THIS IS A GIRL?

UH-HUH...

PROVE IT.

IT'S OKAY, SHHH . . .

WAAAAAAAAAAAAAAAAAAAAAAHHHHHHH

pat pat

SO YOU'RE NAMING HER **DANA**, RIGHT? TO RHYME WITH RAINA? SO WE MATCH?

ACTUALLY . . .

. . . I'D LIKE TO CALL HER **AMARA**.

WHAT? WHAT KIND OF NAME IS **THAT?!**

AAAAAAAAAAAAAAAAAAA

IT MEANS "IMMORTAL" IN SANSKRIT, AND "LOVE" IN LATIN.

WHAAAAAAAAHHH

IT ALSO MEANS "BITTER ONE," BUT YOUR MOM LIKES IT, SO THAT'S THAT.

pat pat

cough

hic

11

GIRLS, HAVE YOU FINISHED PACKING?

WE LEAVE FIRST THING IN THE MORNING! **GO!**

WHAT DO PEOPLE EVEN WEAR IN COLORADO?

WILL MY COUSINS THINK MY CLOTHES ARE COOL?

Knock Knock

Aptos Tigers

YES?

ARE YOU HAVING A FASHION SHOW IN HERE OR SOMETHING?

WHAT? NO! DON'T COME IN!

I STILL DON'T SEE WHY MOM AND DAD GAVE **YOU** YOUR OWN ROOM.

BECAUSE I'M STARTING HIGH SCHOOL NEXT MONTH, AND I NEED MY PRIVACY.

THAT'S DUMB. ANYWAY, DO YOU HAVE ANY COLORED PENCILS?

WHAT FOR?

THE TRIP. WE'RE GONNA BE IN THE CAR FOR A WHOLE WEEK IN BOTH DIRECTIONS.

NOPE, NO COLORED PENCILS **HERE**. NOW GET OUT.

I GUESS WE **WILL** BE PRETTY BORED IN THE CAR....

YANK

BURY

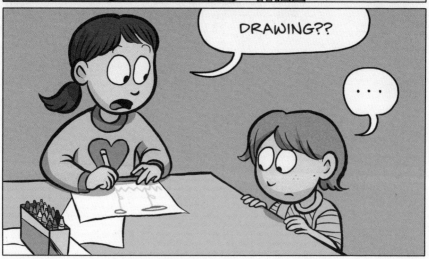

DAW?

YEAH! YOU WANNA DRAW?

HERE --

SNATCH!

SCRIBBLE COLOR SCRIBBLE SCRIBBLE

NO! NO! NOT OVER **MY** DRAWING!!

SCRIBBLE SCRIBBLE

HERE, HAVE YOUR OWN PAPER.

Draw
Scribble
Draw Draw

YOU CAN SIT AT THE TABLE AND DRAW WITH ME, Y'KNOW.

Draw
Scribble
Scribble

Draw
Draw
Draw

20

AMARA, WHY DON'T YOU SIT AT THE DRAWING TABLE WITH YOUR SISTER?

C'MON, HONEY --

NO TOUCH!!

NO NO NO NO NO NO NO NO NOOOOOOOOOO!!!

YOU CAN SIT WHEREVER YOU WANT TO. I DON'T CARE.

WHATEVER MAKES YOU HAPPY.

sniff

27

ANATOMY of a ROAD TRIP
<stuff>
Fruit Snacks
Paper
Amara's Wild Kingdom
National Geographic
Pens
Pencils
Road Atlas
Raina's Radical Zone
Chips
Walkman
Pillow
Lynda Barry Comics
Bear
Teen Mags
Little Brother Section
Mom's Corner
Juice pouch
Mom-bag
Skater Magazines
Map
Cars
Trucks
Baby carrots
Instant coffee in Thermos

crunch
crunch

IT'S GETTING HOT, MOM.

I KNOW. I'M SORRY MY CAR DOESN'T HAVE AIR-CONDITIONING.

BUT I CAN OPEN A WINDOW!

WHOOSH

squeaky squeaky

~~~~~~~!

WHAT???

YOU'D HEAR BETTER WITHOUT THOSE STUPID HEADPHONES ON.

WHAT?

YOU'D HEAR --

NEVER MIND.

Listen and Learn

RRRRRRT

HEY!

OUR STORY BEGINS IN A DEEP, WOODED THICKET...

OUR STORY BEGINS IN A DEEP, WOODED THICKET...

HI, GIRLS. WHAT ARE YOU DRAWING TODAY?

I'M DRAWING A FLOWER AND A SUN!

NICE, RAINA.

I DAWING A GIZZLY BEAR BY A STREAM, AN' A DEER, AN' A EAGLE, AN' ANOTHER DEER . . . AND OVER HERE . . .

TODAY WE DRIVE ACROSS NEVADA!

THE SILVER STATE.

LOOKS MORE LIKE THE BROWN STATE.

OR THE BURNT SIENNA STATE.

CLOSER TO RAW UMBER.

OR MAYBE BEIGE.

KHAKI?

SO . . . ABOUT THOSE COLORED PENCILS . . .

AWW, MAN! MY BATTERIES ARE DEAD!

AMARA, CAN I BORROW YOUR WALKMAN?

CAN I BORROW **YOUR** COLORED PENCILS?

GIRLS! CALM DOWN. WE'LL GET BATTERIES AT THE NEXT GAS STATION.

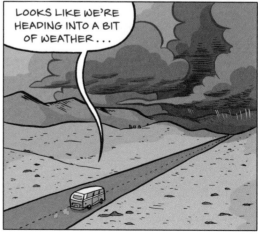

LOOKS LIKE WE'RE HEADING INTO A BIT OF WEATHER . . .

THE WIND REALLY PICKED UP!!

AND THE ROAD'S SO SLICK, I HAVE TO BE CAREFUL WE DON'T --

Squeak Squeak

HYDROPLANE!!!

AHHHHH!!

SLIIIIIIIIIIIIIIIIIIDE~

≋GASP≋ I CAN BARELY SEE FIVE FEET AHEAD!

WE'RE GOING TO PULL OVER AND WAIT THIS STORM OUT.

Whew.

WHAT'S THE NAME OF THIS TOWN, MOM?

UH ... WE'RE IN LOVELOCK, NEVADA.

AREA CODE 666, I PRESUME?

47

THE NEXT MORNING

OOF.

IS IT STILL RAINING?

I DON'T THINK SO. . . .

Peek!

EW, LOOK.

AND SO:

I'M CALLING MINE BUBBLY.

I'M CALLING MINE ROSEMARIE.

YOUR FISH POOED!

ALL FISH POO, RAINA.

BUBBLY'S POO IS THE GROSSEST.

IT'S ALMOST TIME TO EAT. WILL YOU GET OUT THE CHIPS AND SALSA, PLEASE?

TORTILLA

THE SALSA LOOKS LIKE IT HAS BUBBLY POO IN IT!!

HA HA HA HA HA HA HA HA

PTOO! PTOO! PTOO! PTOO!

53

NO! DON'T FLUSH HIM!

WHAT SHOULD WE DO INSTEAD?

here Lies Bubbly

THE NEXT DAY

WHAT ARE YOU GOING TO CALL YOUR NEW FISH, AMARA?

HMM...

BOBOLI! LIKE THE PIZZA!!

DON'T RUIN **PIZZA** FOR ME, TOO, AMARA!!

BUT SOON

here lies Bubbly
Here lies BoboLi
here lies Rose-marie

I'M SORRY, GIRLS.... I GUESS THE WHOLE FISH THING DIDN'T WORK OUT.

BUT IT'S NOT LIKE IT WAS YOUR FAULT THEY KEPT DYING....

FISH ARE JUST DELICATE.

MAYBE YOU NEED A **HEARTIER** PET.

A DOG?

A HAIRLESS CAT?

...A CHAMELEON??

COOOOOOL!!

DON'T WORRY! MY BUDDY FRANK BREEDS 'EM. HE SAYS THEY'RE PRETTY INDESTRUCTIBLE.

Veterans Upward Bound

AT THE PET STORE

THEY EAT CRICKETS??

UH-HUH, AND WE'RE HAVING A SALE! FIVE DOLLARS FOR TWENTY!

Flea Flea   Flea

Rabbit Feed   Bunny Chow   Hop Fuel

THIS SEEMS LIKE A LOT OF CRICKETS, DAD....

chirp chirp chirp chirp chirp chir chirp chirp chirp chirp chirp ch chirp chir chirp chirp chirp ch chirp chir

YEP! LELAND'S GONNA BE IN FOODIE PARADISE!

chirp chirp chirp chirp chirp chirp chirp Ch Chir chi

HE STILL HASN'T EATEN ANY.

MAYBE HE'S A LITTLE INTIMIDATED.

BUT I'LL BET THAT, BY MORNING, HE'LL HAVE EATEN A FEW.

Tweet Tweet ♫♪

Blink

AAAAAAAUUGH!!!

WHAT THE **HECK?!**

chirp chirp chirp Chirp chirp Chirp Chirp chirp chirp irp chirp

THE **CRICKETS** ATE **LELAND?!**

THEY SUCKED ALL HIS GUTS RIGHT OUT!!!

chirp chirp chirp

LICENSE PLATE BINGO

ABC1234 ALABAMA	HAWAII ABC 123 ALOHA STATE	Massachusetts 12AB34	123 ABC New Mexico USA	1AB 234 SouthDakota
ALASKA ABC 123	scenic IDAHO 1A B234 FAMOUS POTATOES	MICHIGAN 1AB C23 Great Lakes	NEW YORK ~~ABC 1234~~	TENNESSEE ABC 123
~~ARIZONA ABC 1234~~	illinois Land of Lincoln AB 1234	Minnesota 123 ABC	First in Flight ABC-1234 NORTH CAROLINA	TEXAS AB1 C23 THE LONE STAR STATE
Arkansas 123 ABC	INDIANA 12AB345	MISSISSIPPI ABC 123	ABC 123 NORTH DAKOTA	UTAH 000 ABC
~~California 1ABC234~~	~~Iowa 123 ABC~~	MISSOURI 123 ABC	OHIO BIRTHPLACE OF AVIATION AAA 0000	Vermont ABC 123
~~ABC~~	KANSAS ABC 123	~~MONTANA 12·1234 BIG SKY~~	OKLAHOMA 123 ABC	VIRGINIA ABC 123
Connecticut ABC	Kentucky 123 ABC Bluegrass State	Nebraska ABC 123	Oregon	
3456 DELAWARE	Lovisiana A123456	~~NEVADA 123 ABC~~	PEN AB	
FLORIDA	MAINE ABCDEF	Live free or die 123 4567 New HAMPSHIRE	Rhode I AB-1 Ocean State	
Maryland ABC 123	~~New Jersey AB 123C Garden State~~	South Carolina 012 ABC	20	

READY TO SEE SOME DINOSAURS, WILL?

YEAH!!

DINOSAURS. DIEEEE-NO-SAUR. DINOOOOOO. DI-DI-DI-DI-DI . . .

Tappity Tappity

Whap Whap

Tap Tap

CAN'T YOU BE EXCITED **QUIETLY?!!!**

Dinosaur National Monument

Visitor Center/Dinosaur Quarry 5 MILES AHEAD

DIEEEE-NO-SAUR . . .

OH MAN, WHY IS UTAH A MILLION DEGREES?

I THOUGHT YOU LOVED HOT WEATHER.

YEAH, BUT I'M NOT **USED** TO IT! SAN FRANCISCO IS FREEZING IN SUMMER.

DINOSAUR NATIONAL MONUMENT FOSSIL BONE QUARRY

IF WE WERE SWIMMING, THIS WOULD BE FINE.

DON'T EVEN THINK ABOUT IT.

AWWWH! CAN I GET THIS TRUCK, MOM??

Dino Dig Vehicle

I SUPPOSE EACH OF YOU CAN CHOOSE **ONE** SOUVENIR.

scratch scratch scratch

Dino Dig Vehicle

?

Tap Tap

OOH! OOH! BACK SCRATCHER!! YES!

WELL, KIDS...

WELCOME TO COLORFUL COLORADO

ONE MORE NIGHT OF CAMPING, AND TOMORROW WE'LL SEE YOUR COUSINS!

VRRRRRRRM!

LET'S SEE...

COLORADO: THE CENTENNIAL STATE.

THAT'S NO FUN.

ROAD ATLAS

SCR EEE EEE EEE!

I WAS HOPING IT WOULD BE, LIKE, "BEARS EAT YOUR LITTLE BROTHER STATE."

YEAH....

NEEEERRR-OWWWWWWW! GSSSHHH! VROOOOOM!!!

YOUR MOM AND I LIKE THE NAME WILL.

WILLY! HI, WILLY!

NOT WILLY. JUST WILL.

AH!

WILLY WAS YOUR GRANDMA'S DOG'S NAME....

?

WHEREAS YOUR BROTHER IS HERE BECAUSE OF THE **WILL OF GOD.**

URRK.

66

DINNNG DONNG ♫

OH, THAT MUST BE THE DELIVERY.

WHAT'S ALL THIS?

↑ THIS END UP

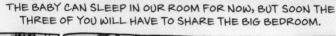

THE BABY CAN SLEEP IN OUR ROOM FOR NOW, BUT SOON THE THREE OF YOU WILL HAVE TO SHARE THE BIG BEDROOM.

THIS IS A BUNK BED!

↑ THIS END UP

↑ THIS END UP

WOULDN'T IT BE EASIER TO JUST MOVE?

≥HIC≤
WAAAA-
AAH...

WAAAH! WAAAH! WAH!

GROOOAN.

I CAN'T SLEEEEP!
WHY DOESN'T MOM
MAKE THAT BABY
BE QUIET?

≥HIC≤ ≥COUGH≤
WAAAAAAHHHH...

IF MOM HAD THAT SUPERPOWER,
I THINK SHE'D USE IT ON YOU,
TOO....

AHWAAAAAA
AAAAHHHH...

crunch
crunch

SLRRRP

crunch
crunch

DENIS, YOU'LL TAKE RAINA TO THE BUS STOP ON YOUR WAY TO WORK?

UH-HUH. READY, RAINA?

ALMOST.

AND I'LL TAKE AMARA TO PRE-SCH--

SWAT

I'M NOT GOING.

IT'S NOT EASY HAVING SO MANY OF US IN ONE HOUSE, HUH?

I DUNNO.

YOUR MOM ASKED ME TO DO SOMETHING WITH YOU AND YOUR SISTER THIS WEEKEND. HOW 'BOUT WE GO TO THE ZOO?

OKAY.

AND SO:

C'MON, A! IT'S DADDY-DAUGHTER DAY.

MMM.

I'M TAKING YOU AND RAINA OUT. JUST THE THREE OF US!

MNH.

WE'RE GOING TO THE ZOO....

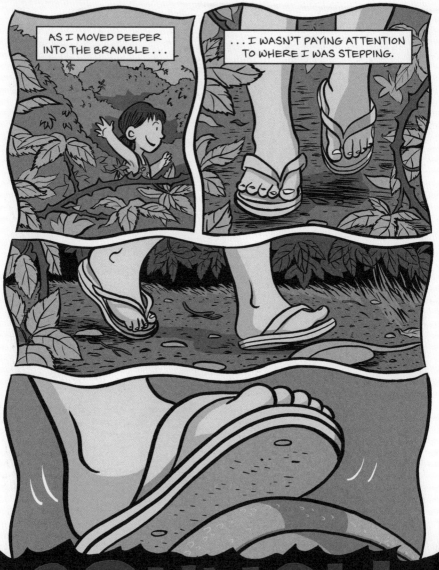

I GUESS STEPPING ON A LIVE SNAKE **IS** KINDA GROSS.

IT WAS DEAD.

IT WAS DEAD?! HA HA HA HA HA HA HA!!!

IT'S NOT FUNNY!!

IT IS **SO**. AND I'M TOTALLY GETTING A SNAKE FOR A PET SOMEDAY.

ARE NOT!

AM SO!

ARE NOT!

HA HA HA HA!!

WHAT'S MOM MAKING FOR DINNER?

MASHED POTATOES AND CUP O' NOODLES.

I AM SO SICK OF MASHED POTATOES AND CUP O' NOODLES.

THAT'S ENOUGH MOPING, EVERYONE.

GET YOUR FLASHLIGHTS -- WE'RE GOING ON A STAR WALK.

A WHAT?

WE HIKE AWAY FROM THE OTHER CAMPSITES . . .

. . . FIND A NICE TREELESS SPOT, AND LIE DOWN . . .

. . . AND TURN OFF OUR FLASHLIGHTS.

CLICK

CLICK
CLICK

GASP!!

THIS IS AMAZING! THIS IS INCREDIBLE! I WISH I COULD TAKE A PICTURE!!

YOUR DAD AND I USED TO DO THIS ALL THE TIME WHEN WE WERE YOUNGER.

I WISH DADDY WAS HERE RIGHT NOW.

I WISH DAD WAS HERE, TOO.

DAD WOULD'VE GOTTEN US McDONALD'S.

...BUT I DON'T **WANT** TACOS!

TOO BAD!

I! WANT! Mc! DONALD'S!

YOU CAN'T **HAVE** MCDONALD'S!

I COULD GO AND GET YOU SOME McDONALD'S....

DENIS!

SHE'S NEVER GOING TO LEARN!

SHE'S NEVER GOING TO STOP SCREAMING!

NO. BOTH OF YOU, **NO.** AMARA, GO TO YOUR ROOM.

HISSSS...

A dream where Dad still has a job...

A dream where we didn't just get a new baby brother...

A dream where I never even got the sister I asked for.

A dream where someone is going to put their arms around me and tell me...

IT'S GOING TO BE OKAY.

LATER

BLAH BLAH JOB SEARCH . . .
BLAH BLAH WANT ADS . . .
BLAH BLAH ECONOMY . . .

MAYBE IT'S TIME I THOUGHT ABOUT FINISHING COLLEGE.

MAYBE.

EW, WHY WOULD ANYONE **WANT** TO GO TO SCHOOL?

TO GET A GOOD JOB.

WHY WOULD ANYONE WANT TO **WORK**?!

TO MAKE MONEY!

DON'T **YOU** WANT TO HAVE MONEY WHEN YOU'RE OLDER?

OF COURSE I DO! I'LL HAVE PLENTY OF MONEY!

HOW?

I'LL SAVE IT IN MY PIGGY BANK.

ACHOO!!

Allergic to trees and dust

HA HA! I LOVE THIS CREEPY ELF!

LOOK, I MADE THIS ONE AT SCHOOL!

≋HONK≋ GIRLS?

X-MAS

YOU KNOW WE CAN'T AFFORD TO BUY TOO MANY PRESENTS THIS YEAR, RIGHT?

IT'S OKAY, DAD.

YEAH.

JUST HAVE **SANTA** BRING THEM ALL!

94

HOW ARE YOUR LETTERS TO SANTA COMING, GIRLS?

GOOD! I ASKED FOR WORLD PEACE, SOME NEW MARKERS, A JOB FOR DAD, AND THE NEWEST BABY-SITTERS CLUB BOOK!

WHAT ABOUT YOU, AMARA?

a SNAKE

ICK! BLECH! GROSS!

YOU MIGHT WANT TO ASK FOR SOMETHING ELSE, HONEY....

MERRY =SNIFF= CHRISTMAS!

FOR Raina from Smith

BASS DRUM CASSETTE

I SEE LONDON,
I SEE FRANCE...

AMARA!!!

AAAAH! AAAAH! AAAHHH!!!

WHAT'S WRONG?! WHAT HAPPENED?

MY EARS!!

OH, YES -- THAT'S FROM THE ALTITUDE. YOU FELL ASLEEP AND YOUR EARS HAVEN'T POPPED.

OW! OW! OW! OW! OW!

TRY HOLDING YOUR NOSE AND CLOSING YOUR MOUTH, THEN BLOW --

SNRK

AAAAAAAAAAA...

AAAAAAAUUUUU...

UUUGGGGGHHH!!!!

ARE THESE ALL NEW HOUSES, MOM?

UH-HUH. I THINK THIS HOUSING DEVELOPMENT IS ABOUT THREE YEARS OLD.

2753 POPLAR COURT . . . THIS IS THE PLACE.

MARY!

HI, SIS.

HI, AUNT MARY. IS LINDSAY AROUND?

SHE WENT TO THE MALL.

OH.

BUT YOUR COUSINS JOSH AND JEREMY GOT HERE THIS MORNING.

YOU DON'T LOOK LIKE A RAINA. . . . I'M GOING TO CALL YOU PENELOPE. DO YOU PLAY CARDS?

SO, PENELOPE, WHAT'S YOUR THING?

MY . . . THING?

YEAH. DO YOU LIKE RAP MUSIC? HORROR MOVIES? *BEVERLY HILLS, 90210?*

OH. I LIKE COMICS!

YEAH?? LIKE BATMAN? HULK? X-MEN?

I LIKE CALVIN AND HOBBES, FOR BETTER OR FOR WORSE, FOXTROT . . .

PSSH. THOSE AREN'T **REAL** COMICS.

SLAM

DAD!

WHEN DID **YOU** GET HERE??

YOUR UNCLE JIM JUST PICKED ME UP AT THE AIRPORT!

SLLLP

DO AMARA AND WILL KNOW YOU'RE HERE?

THEY'RE BOTH ASLEEP. YOU MUST BE PRETTY TIRED, TOO!

YAWWWN . . . YEAH, MAYBE I'LL GO GET READY FOR --

KARAOKE PARTY!!!

WHO'S IN??

MAYBE I'LL GO GET READY FOR A KARAOKE PARTY??

WOOO!

AND SO:

CHECK OUT WHAT MY JOB SENT HOME WITH ME, EVERYONE....

512K enhanced

CLICK THIS... OPEN THIS HERE... LOAD THIS UP...

Tick Tap Tap

OOOOOOOOH!

124

Hee hee   Giggle

Ha Ha!
Snort

PENELOPE STILL SLEEPS WITH A TEDDY BEAR!!

Ha Ha

Ha Ha

HUH?? WHAT ARE YOU GUYS DOING IN HERE?

UH, THIS IS MY DEN? WE'RE EATING BREAKFAST.

WHAT ARE YOU -- THIRTEEN?

I'M FOURTEEN.

HAAAAAAA HA HA HA HA HA HA!!

I DON'T CARE ABOUT THIS STUPID BEAR! MY SISTER PROBABLY PACKED HIM.

MMM-HMM.

I'LL PROVE IT.

FLING!

WHUMP!

I'M SO SORRY!

LINDSAY SURE HAS A LOT OF BEAUTY PRODUCTS. . . .

EW, WHAT DID YOU DO TO YOUR FACE?!

OKAY IF I SIT WITH YOU GUYS?

SO, LINDSAY! ARE YOU STILL INTO SKATING?

HUH?

ANYWAY. JEREMY, HAVE YOU SEEN THE NEW GUNS N' ROSES VIDEO?

YES.

BLAH BLAH HEAVY METAL . . . BLAH BLAH LEATHER FASHIONS . . . BLAH BLAH BIG HAIR . . .

Ha ha.

HAAAAAHAHAHAHA!! GNARLY! HIGH FIVE!!

Ha Ha Ha Ha Ha

SORRY, PENELOPE -- WE'RE HALFWAY THROUGH THIS GAME. WE'LL DEAL YOU IN NEXT TIME, OKAY?

≡SIGH≡

HEY, LISTEN . . .

I . . . I **DID** BRING COLORED PENCILS ON THIS TRIP. I HID THEM IN MY SUITCASE.

YOU WANT TO USE THEM? I'LL TOTALLY GO GET THEM FOR YOU.

NAH.

LIKE I SAID . . . I DON'T REALLY CARE.

SIGH . . . THE COUSIN I WISHED WAS MY SISTER BARELY KNOWS ME AT ALL.

AND THE SISTER I ACTUALLY HAVE HATES ME.

ALTHOUGH I GUESS IT'S NOTHING PERSONAL . . .

SHE HATES EVERYONE.

KIDS, YOUR MOM AND I HAVE MADE AN EXECUTIVE DECISION.

I KNOW WE'VE ALL BEEN CRAMPED AND CROWDED IN THIS LITTLE APARTMENT FOR YEARS. . . .

AND YOU GUYS WOULD ALL LIKE A BIT OF EXTRA PRIVACY, SO --

WE'RE MOVING?!

WE'VE DECIDED TO GIVE RAINA HER OWN BEDROOM.

OH.

...OH. **OH!!!**

NO FAIR!!

BUT I STILL HAFTA SHARE A ROOM WITH WILL?!

RAINA'S GROWING UP, HONEY. SHE NEEDS SOME SPACE.

WAIT, WE ONLY HAVE TWO BEDROOMS.... WHERE ARE YOU AND DAD GONNA SLEEP?

WE'LL MOVE INTO THE LIVING ROOM.

WOW, YOU'D DO THAT FOR ME?

YOU'D DO THAT FOR HER?!

WE KNEW YOU'D FEEL A LITTLE PUT OUT BECAUSE OF ALL THIS, AMARA . . .

SO, WE'RE GOING TO BUY YOU THAT SNAKE YOU'VE BEEN WANTING.

WHAT?!

144

New Home Layout:

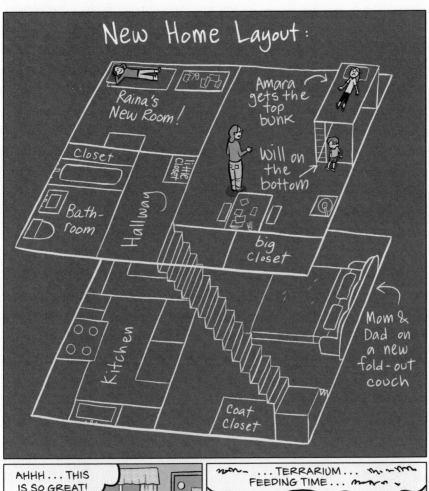

Raina's New Room!

Closet

Bath-room

Hallway

little Closet

Amara gets the top bunk

Will on the bottom

big closet

Mom & Dad on a new fold-out couch

Kitchen

Coat Closet

AHHH ... THIS IS SO GREAT!

... TERRARIUM ... FEEDING TIME ...

TOO BAD THE WALLS AREN'T THICKER!

AAAAAAUGH! HE'S CRAWLING OUT!!!

HE'S, HE'S . . .

HE'S CLIMBING UP INTO THE CAR SEAT!!

GRAB HIM!!

NO WAY! HE'LL **BITE** ME!!

WE HAVE TO DO SOMETHING!

THERE'S A SNAKE IN THE VAN?!?!

BUT AREN'T YOU GLAD WE TOLD YOU **AFTER** PICKING YOU UP FROM GIRL SCOUTS?

AAAAAA AAA

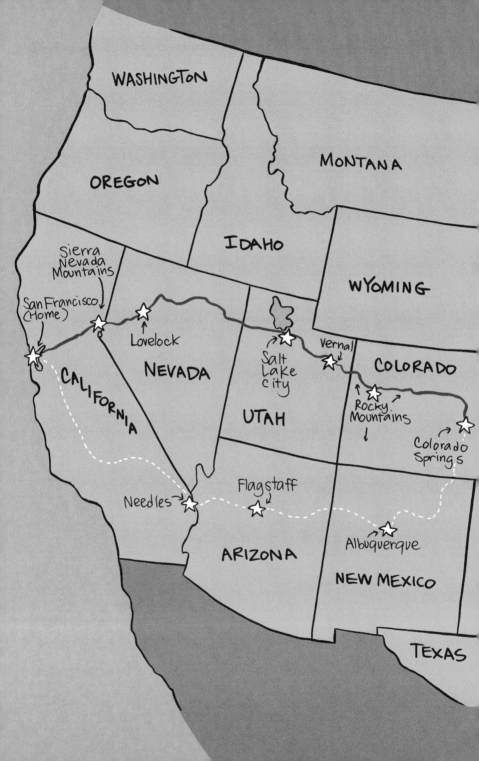

Sssssssss...

Sssssssss S...

SSSSSSSSSS...

SNAKE?!!

IT'S JUST UNCLE BILL FRYING BACON, YOU MORON.

SSS SSSS

crunch
crunch

Ssss sss

SO YOU'RE LEAVING TODAY, HUH?

YEAH. ANY PARTING WORDS OF WISDOM?

'BOUT WHAT?

I DUNNO. I START HIGH SCHOOL IN TWO WEEKS. ANY ADVICE?

I GUESS ... UH ... DON'T BE AS NERDY AS JOSH, HERE?

EXCUSE ME, LINSEED, BEING THE TOWN PINOCHLE CHAMPION IS CONSIDERED **COOL** WHERE I'M FROM.

YOU ALWAYS HAVE TO STEAL MY THUNDER!!

WHATEVER -- YOU HAVEN'T DRAWN ALL WEEK!

SO?!

GIRLS, YOU ARE **BOTH** ARTISTS! ALWAYS HAVE BEEN, ALWAYS WILL BE. YOU HAVE THAT IN **COMMON**.

WHY CAN'T YOU TWO GET ALONG?

YOU JUST SPENT A WEEK ARGUING WITH **YOUR** BROTHERS AND SISTERS.

LET'S GO.

HOW IS THAT DIFFERENT?

YEAH!

NO, REALLY, MOM, EXPLAIN!

YEAH, WE'RE LISTENING!

SIGH

156

157

DENIS, YOU **KNOW** WE HAVE EVERYTHING WE NEED.

I JUST --

YOU WORRY TOO MUCH! WE'LL BE FINE.

FLIGHT 56 IS NOW BOARDING FOR SAN FRANCISCO....

NOW GO HOME AND WATCH BASEBALL ALL WEEK, AND GRIND YOUR COFFEE AS EARLY IN THE MORNING AS YOU PLEASE.

#56 San Fra...co 12:40p

...

...

NOW YOU KNOW THE **REAL** REASON I CAN'T RIDE HOME WITH YOU, WILL.

ANOTHER WEEK IN THE CAR. **FUN.**

IT'LL BE INTERESTING, RAINA. . . .

WE'RE GOING TO DRIVE HOME ALONG THE **SOUTHERN** ROUTE!

SO IT'LL BE EVEN HOTTER?

KNOCK
KNOCK

DID YOU GET THE SNAKE OUT OF THE CAR?

NOT YET.

THEN I'M NOT COMING OUT.

YOU CAN'T STAY IN YOUR ROOM FOREVER!

She lured me out with cookies

OKAY. LET ME GET THIS STRAIGHT....

MANGO IS A KING SNAKE, AND KING SNAKES ONLY EAT **LIVE** MICE....

UH-HUH.

HEY, MOM?

UH-HUH?

I JUST REALIZED YOU NEVER KISSED DAD GOOD-BYE. HOW COME?

. . .

AND WHEN HE SAID HE'D DRIVE YOU CRAZY...

... THAT WAS JUST A JOKE, RIGHT?

RAINA, DON'T BE AN IDIOT.

HEY! I'M NOT AN IDIOT! I'M JUST ASKING A QUESTION!

AN **IDIOTIC** QUESTION!

THAT'S OKAY....

YOUR DAD AND I... WELL, WE...

WE WANTED TO SPEND SOME TIME APART THIS SUMMER.

I THOUGHT HE COULDN'T DRIVE WITH US BECAUSE OF **WORK!**

THAT'S PART OF THE REASON, TOO.

CHILL OUT, WOULD YOU?

CHILL OUT? **CHILL OUT?!**

WE'RE IN THE MIDDLE OF NOWHERE... IT'S A MILLION DEGREES...

MOM AND WILL ARE OUT THERE WITH GOD KNOWS WHO, AND NOW...

BEEEEEEEEEEOOP.

!

AND NOW MY STUPID WALKMAN'S DEAD AGAIN!!

FLING!

WOULD IT BE THE END OF THE WORLD FOR YOU TO **NOT** HAVE YOUR WALKMAN ON FOR A FEW HOURS?!

YES.

WHAT IF MOM SERIOUSLY NEVER COMES BACK?

WOULDN'T **THAT** BE WORSE?

AMARA?

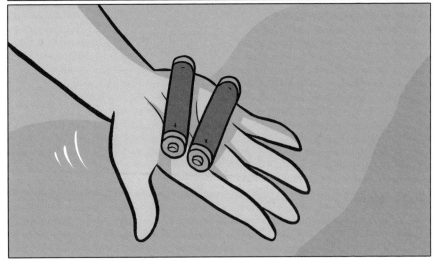

CATRINA'S AUTO REPAIR

FLATS FIXED

EAT **NOM** GRUB **YUM** SNARF SHOVEL

GIRLS, I AM **SO SORRY.**

I DON'T KNOW WHAT I WAS THINKING!

LEAVING YOU TWO ALL ALONE . . . WHAT IF SOMETHING HAD HAPPENED TO YOU?

IT'S OKAY, MOM.

FINDING A RIDE FOR FOUR WOULD'VE BEEN HARDER THAN TWO.

Tired Tires!

TRY NEW McLean Deluxe

AND ANYWAY, WE SURVIVED! RIGHT, RAINA?

BARELY.

... and then Mango crawled right out of the
Raina was totally mortified, but I was brave
trapped him in a grocery bag. We stuck him
in your suitcase. I hope that's okay. We th
your clothes in the grocery bag! Then w
waited another hour and you and Will ca
back. So now we can bring Mango hor
it's perfect! The terrarium is all rea
and waiting for him! And I promise
I'll feed him the mice. You don't have to

What an amazing story! Your dad is going to freak out when he hears this. Let ME tell him, okay? Wow! Mango should be called a camel snake, not a king s

Maybe the newspaper wi to write a sto about Mango! even the n w t abou the ra bet K even co

Photo Album

After I wrote the script for this book, my dad sent me this photo, which I had forgotten about. This picture pretty much encapsulates *Sisters* in a nutshell. We're about six and one here.

My mom took this picture of Amara and me sitting on top of a hamper in our upstairs hallway. The photo still hangs in the same spot.

Goldfish. We look pretty excited, don't we?

Here we are around the time this book takes place: ages fourteen, nine, and six. Amara had just won first place in an art contest I'd gotten an honorable mention for, a few years prior. I'm hiding my jealousy well!

Thanks to . . .

My family, obviously: my mom, dad, brother, sister, aunts, uncles, cousins, and grandparents. Thank you for letting me mine our collective history (and photo albums) for story ideas!

My husband, Dave Roman, who is invaluable in every way.

My editors David Saylor and Cassandra Pelham, and the tireless team at Scholastic: Sheila Marie Everett, Lizette Serrano, Candace Greene, Phil Falco, Bess Braswell, Whitney Steller, Tracy van Straaten, Ed Masessa, David Levithan, Lori Benton, Ellie Berger, John Mason, Antonio Gonzalez, Emily Heddleson, Starr Baer, Jaime Capifali, and all the wonderful folks whose time and space dovetail with mine.

My agent, Judy Hansen, for working her magic.

Braden Lamb, for his stellar coloring.

John Green, for tech wizardry and his nifty lettering.

Jerzy and Anne Drozd, my beta readers.

My wonderful fans, who keep me smiling, and make it all worthwhile.